D0655234

Hercules
The World's Strongest Man

Retold by Alex Frith

Illustrated by Linda Cavallini

Reading consultant: Alison Kelly
Roehampton University

Contents

Hercules was born in Ancient Greece, and
was known then as Heracles. But his story
was spread all over the world by the Ancient
Romans, who called him Hercules.

Chapter 1

"What have I done?"

Hercules was a strong, brave and cheerful man. But today he sat with his head in his hands, sobbing.

"What have I done?" he groaned. "My wife and children are dead, and it's all my fault!"

The night before, Hercules had eaten a great feast. But he didn't know that the goddess Hera had poisoned his wine.

The poison drove Hercules crazy. As he was eating, he thought he saw his family turn into wild animals – and so he killed them.

Hera was the wife of Zeus, the king of the gods. Hercules was Zeus's son, and Zeus adored him – but Hera was not his mother. Hera hated Hercules.

Hercules desperately wanted to be a hero. But how could he, after what he'd done? He went to a temple to pray to his father, Zeus.

"Hercules, I am ashamed of you!" bellowed Zeus. "But I will forgive you, if you can prove your strength, courage and determination."

"Go to King Eurystheus in Tiryns. He will set you ten tasks. You must complete them all."

Eurystheus was a loyal servant of Hera. Hercules knew the tasks wouldn't be easy.

7

Chapter 2

Wild beasts

"Your first task is to kill the Nemean Lion," said King Eurystheus, "and bring back its skin as proof."

Hercules picked up a bow and some arrows, a sword and a wooden club. Then he set off for the town of Nemea to find the lion.

When he arrived, the Nemeans laughed at him. "You'll never kill the lion," they said. "It has such a tough skin that no weapon can pierce it."

Sure enough, when Hercules fired an arrow at the lion, it bounced off. He hit it with his sword, but the blade bent. So he smashed the wooden club on its head.

BONK!

The lion was stunned. Hercules quickly grabbed the lion's neck in his mighty arms.

He squeezed tight until the lion
was dead. But he couldn't cut off
its skin with his sword. Instead, he
used the lion's own sharp claws.

Hercules tied the skin around his
neck. The first task was complete.

"I can see that you're strong enough to kill a simple lion," said King Eurystheus. "But can you kill the terrifying hydra of Lernea?"

The hydra was a creature with many long, snake-like heads. Each one spat poisonous venom.

Hercules was feeling brave. He even asked his nephew Iolaus to come along and watch this task.

Together they headed for Lernea and the cave where the hydra lived.

Hercules set fire to some branches just in front of the cave. Thick smoke billowed into the cavemouth. The hydra poked a head out to see what was happening.

Hercules was waiting. With one swipe of his sword he slashed off the hydra's head. "This is easy!" he said to Iolaus.

But then something astonishing happened. Two new heads grew out of the wound in the hydra's neck and they spat dark venom at Hercules.

"What can I do?" shouted Hercules, as he dodged the venom. "I'll never be able to kill the hydra if it keeps growing new heads."

Iolaus had an idea. He grabbed one of the burning branches. "Quick, uncle," he called. "Cut off another head."

As soon as the head came off, Iolaus set fire to the stump. No new heads could grow.

Together, Hercules and Iolaus cut off and burned every one of the hydra's heads.

Before heading home, Hercules took out a few arrows and dipped them in the hydra's venom.

Poison arrows might come in handy one day.

Chapter 3

Run, Hercules, run

"That last task doesn't count!" shouted Eurystheus. "Iolaus helped you, and that's cheating." But secretly, Eurystheus was impressed.

"You've proved that you're strong and brave, but are you quick enough to catch the Erymanthian boar?"

The boar was a large, unfriendly creature that lived at the bottom of Mount Erymanthus.

Hercules chased the boar all the way up the mountain, but he couldn't catch it.

After a whole day, Hercules was exhausted, but he didn't give up.

At last, the boar jumped to the very top of the mountain. It landed in a patch of snow and slipped.

Hercules pounced on the boar, and quickly tied it up. He proudly dragged it back to Tiryns.

"Take it away!" screamed King Eurystheus, jumping into a giant pot to hide.

"Boars are foolish creatures, anyway. Your next task will be much tougher. Catch the Ceryneian deer – the fastest animal on earth!"

Hercules chased the deer from one end of the world to the other, but he couldn't catch it.

He tried shooting arrows at it, but the deer was so fast, it outran every arrow.

Finally, after an entire year of running, the deer stopped for a drink.

Hercules hid in a bush. Very quietly, he fired an arrow.

The arrow stuck fast into the deer's back leg. Hercules pounced on it to tie it up, and carried the deer back to Tiryns.

Chapter 4

Dirty work

"That task took you a whole year!" laughed King Eurystheus. "For your next task, go and clean out the stables of King Augeas – in a single day."

How hard can that be?

King Augeas was delighted to see Hercules. "My stables are the filthiest in the land," he said. "Are you really going to clean them up in a single day?"

Hercules was very confident. "I bet you I can do it," he boasted.

"If you manage it, I'll give you a hundred of my cows," said Augeas.

Inside the stables, piles of mucky manure towered high, and it smelled disgusting. But Hercules set to work with a shovel, smiling.

After a hour, he stopped smiling. There was simply too much muck. Hercules rested on the shovel and looked through a window in the stables. Just outside, he saw a river.

Hercules had an idea. Using the shovel, he knocked a big hole in the wall. Then he opened the doors.

He began to dig a long ditch. By noon, it reached from the stables all the way to the river.

Next, he found a massive boulder, and dropped it into the river. The water hit the boulder and ran off into the ditch. Soon, great floods of water swept through the stables, washing out all the muck in an instant.

Augeas gasped in amazement.

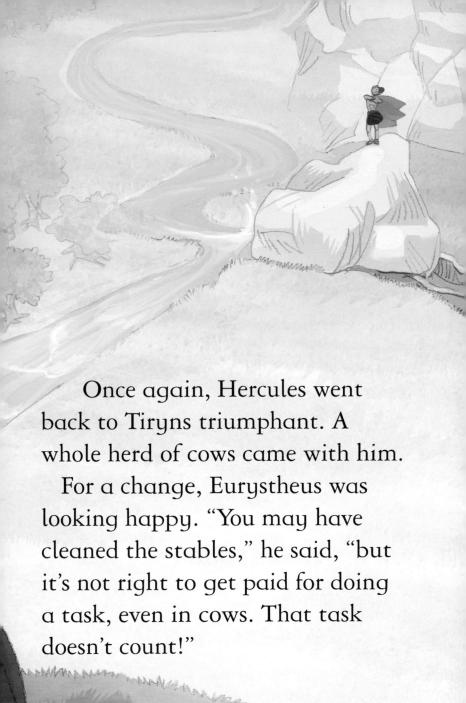

Once again, Hercules went back to Tiryns triumphant. A whole herd of cows came with him.

For a change, Eurystheus was looking happy. "You may have cleaned the stables," he said, "but it's not right to get paid for doing a task, even in cows. That task doesn't count!"

Chapter 5

Dangerous animals

Hercules was feeling stronger and more heroic with each task. But because two didn't count, he still had another seven to do.

Eurystheus quickly thought up three more tasks for Hercules.

First, he had to shoot down
a flock of deadly birds in the
forest of Stymphalia.

They tried to scratch Hercules
with their feathers and claws,
which were made of sharp bronze.
Luckily, he was protected by the
skin of the Nemean lion.

Then, he went to the island of Crete to tame a fire-breathing bull. Throwing a lasso, he snagged its neck and held on tight. Hercules leaped up into the air, and landed with a thump on the bull's back.

After that trick, he captured
five fearsome man-eating mares,
which belonged to the wicked
King Diomedes.

Diomedes tried to feed Hercules
to his mares, but Hercules
outwitted him. He trapped the
king in his own stables.

The hungry mares ate Diomedes and fell asleep. Hercules tied them up and dragged them to Tiryns.

Hera had been watching Hercules complete his tasks. She was not at all happy, and spoke angrily to Eurystheus.

"Hercules must not finish all his tasks," said Hera. "I don't want him to become a hero."

"But he's so brave and strong," replied Eurystheus. "I can't think of any harder tasks to set him."

As usual, it's all up to me.

"Hmm," said Hera. "He's hunted all sorts of animals, and outwitted a man, but let's see how well he does against a new kind of enemy – a woman!"

Chapter 6

Hercules and the women

Eurystheus summoned Hercules
to his court. "For your ninth task,
go to the island of the Amazons,
where only women are allowed,
and steal the belt worn by
Hippolyta, their queen."

Hercules set off for the island,
watched by Hera. As he rowed,
he tried to think of a clever way
to sneak onto the island, but
he had no ideas.

When he arrived, he found Queen Hippolyta herself, waiting for him on the shore.

"Are you the famous Hercules, who killed the lion and the hydra?" she asked.

"Most men are weak, but you must be strong. We want to hear all about your tasks. Come onto our island and eat dinner with us."

At dinner, Hercules soon
charmed Hippolyta with his tales
of bravery, strength and cunning.
She was so impressed that she gave
him her belt to take home.

39

This made one of the dinner
guests furious. It was Hera,
disguised as an Amazon warrior.

Hera whispered into the ear of the
woman next to her. "See how close
he is to our queen. He doesn't want
her belt – he wants to kidnap her!"

Very quickly, the lie spread around the room. Hercules looked up from his food to see a crowd of angry faces.

Hercules charged out of the room. Fighting his way to the beach, he managed to jump back into his boat – just in time.

Chapter 7

Far off lands

Hercules was exhausted. He had
hoped to rest before his tenth task
began, but Eurystheus didn't want
to wait. "Go to the island where
the monster Geryon lives," he said.
"And bring me his cows."

Wearily, Hercules got back into his boat. It was a blazing hot day and Hercules shouted angrily at Helios, the god of the sun. He was so angry, he took out an arrow and shot it at him.

Helios caught the arrow. He felt sorry for Hercules. "Take my golden boat," he said. "It's strong enough to carry the sun, and it will help you cross the ocean."

Thank you!

Even in Helios's boat, it took Hercules months to reach Geryon's island. By the time he arrived, he was rested and ready to fight.

His first challenge was Geryon's two-headed dog. Hercules struck the beast with his wooden club and the dog flew into the sea.

HOOOOOWL!

With the same club, he knocked Geryon's servant into the ground.

Then a huge shadow fell over Hercules. He looked up and saw Geryon for the first time. He couldn't believe his eyes.

Geryon had three ugly heads and six bulging arms on one body.

46

It was as if three ogres had become one gigantic, hideous monster...

Geryon roared at Hercules with his three mouths, and pointed three swords at him.

Hercules ran away.

As Geryon chased after him, Hercules reached behind his back and pulled out a special arrow.

It was one of the arrows he had dipped into the hydra's venom.

Hercules fired a single shot. He watched as the arrow pierced Geryon through one neck, then another, then a third. The monster was dead.

But the task wasn't over.
Hercules arrived back in Tiryns
with all Geryon's cows...

...only to find Hera waiting for him.
She was disguised as a mosquito,
and she stung the cows so hard,
they panicked and ran away.
It took Hercules nearly a year to
round them all up again.

"I told you!" said Eurystheus to Hera. "Hercules really is too strong, and too determined."

"You're right," said Hera, grudgingly. "But he still has to complete two more tasks. Let's give him something impossible to do."

"Send him to pick an apple from the tree of the Hesperides."

Hercules didn't even know where to start. The Hesperides were magical women who tended the garden of the gods. But only the gods knew where the garden was.

Hercules knew of just one person who had dared to share the secrets of the gods – a giant, named Prometheus.

Long ago, Prometheus had told humans the secret of making fire. But Zeus had punished him by chaining him to a mountain and sending vultures to attack him.

Hercules found Prometheus, shot the vultures, and cut off his chains – and the giant was happy to help. "I don't know where the garden is, but my brother, Atlas, does," he said.

Everyone knew Atlas. He lived at the top of the tallest mountain on earth, holding up the sky.

Hercules made the long journey to find him.

"Oh, I know where the garden of the gods is," said Atlas. "But I can't tell you."

"I'll make you a deal," said Hercules.

"If you go to the garden yourself, and fetch me an apple, I'll stay here and hold up the sky for you."

Atlas agreed. He was desperate to stand up straight and stretch his aching muscles.

Meanwhile, Hercules heaved and groaned under the weight of the sky. He couldn't believe how heavy it was. But he didn't dare drop it.

At last, Atlas returned with an apple. "Hercules," he said, "you're doing such a good job I think you should stay. Just for a year or so."

"Of course," said Hercules. "But the sky keeps slipping. Would you show me the best way to hold it?"

As soon as Atlas took hold of the sky, Hercules grabbed the apple and ran down the mountain.

Chapter 8

The final task

Eurystheus was flabbergasted. Not only was Hercules strong enough to hold up the sky, he was cunning enough to outwit Atlas.

But even Hercules couldn't go to the underworld and back, could he? For the final task, Eurystheus sent Hercules down into Hades, the land of the dead. To prove he'd been, he had to bring back Cerberus, a three-headed guard dog who kept the dead from leaving.

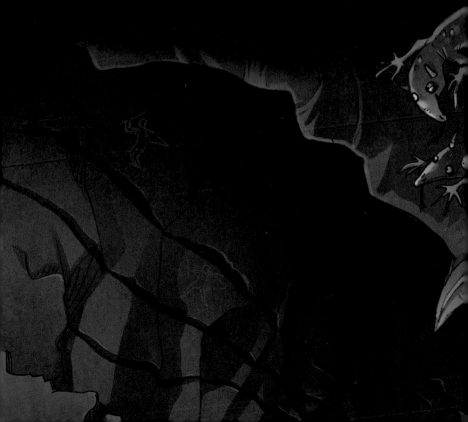

First, Hercules had to cross the murky river Styx, but Charon, the ferryman, wouldn't take him.

"I am Hercules, slayer of beasts and men," boasted Hercules. "I go where I choose. Now take me across into Hades!"

Charon was so scared that he didn't argue.

Gulp!

No sooner had Hercules jumped out of the boat on the other side, than a spooky figure appeared in front of him. It was Persephone, the queen of Hades.

"I've only come for Cerberus," said Hercules with a friendly grin. "I won't stay."

Stop! You do not belong here.

"If you can defeat Cerberus with your bare hands, I will let you borrow him. But you must let him go afterwards," said Persephone.

It was the fight of Hercules's life...

...but he won.

"Well done, Hercules," said King Eurystheus. "You have proved that you are a mighty hero, the strongest, bravest man on earth!"

"Now go out into the world," bellowed Zeus. "You are forgiven."

A hero's life

Even when he was a
tiny baby, Hera plotted
to kill Hercules. She
dropped a snake into
his crib one night...

...but Hercules
strangled it
with his bare
hands.

Before he began his twelve tasks, Hercules had already killed giants and sea monsters.

It took him ten years to complete all the tasks. Afterwards, he went on a long adventure with his friends Jason and the Argonauts.

Legend says that when Hercules died, he became a god.

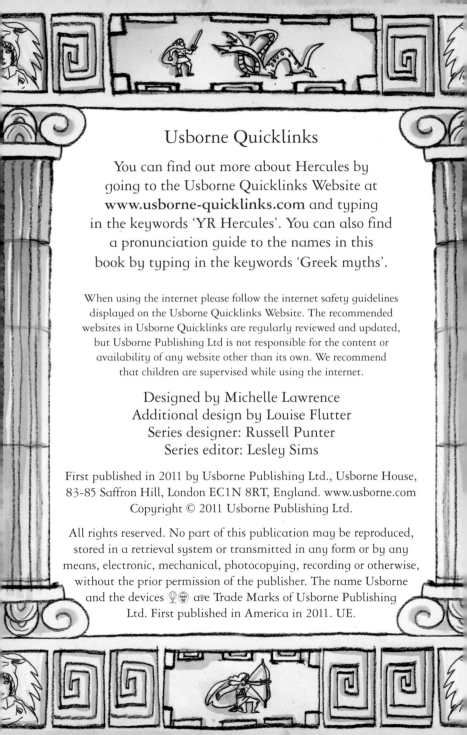

Usborne Quicklinks

You can find out more about Hercules by
going to the Usborne Quicklinks Website at
www.usborne-quicklinks.com and typing
in the keywords 'YR Hercules'. You can also find
a pronunciation guide to the names in this
book by typing in the keywords 'Greek myths'.

When using the internet please follow the internet safety guidelines
displayed on the Usborne Quicklinks Website. The recommended
websites in Usborne Quicklinks are regularly reviewed and updated,
but Usborne Publishing Ltd is not responsible for the content or
availability of any website other than its own. We recommend
that children are supervised while using the internet.

Designed by Michelle Lawrence
Additional design by Louise Flutter
Series designer: Russell Punter
Series editor: Lesley Sims

First published in 2011 by Usborne Publishing Ltd., Usborne House,
83-85 Saffron Hill, London EC1N 8RT, England. www.usborne.com
Copyright © 2011 Usborne Publishing Ltd.